Taro and the Stag Beetle

Written by Mio Debnam

Illustrated by Nathalia Takeyama

Collins

Taro's family all caught a plane to Japan to go to Grandma's funeral.

"She wasn't here to see her tulips bloom," wept Grandpa.

After, Taro's father talked to Grandpa. "We want you to live with us in London," he said. Grandpa paused and looked down. "That's a large decision," he mumbled.

Grandpa moved, a few months later.

"Here's your room," said Taro, cheerfully.

Grandpa's severe expression didn't change as he nodded at Taro. He didn't care that Taro now had to share baby Kiko's room.

Grandpa wouldn't eat the delicious food Mum made. He wouldn't watch television. He just sat with his eyes closed.

"Give him time, he's mourning," said Mum.

"What's mourning?" asked Taro.

"He's sad about Grandma," Mum explained.

Taro told knock-knock jokes, got out his robots, and challenged Grandpa to thumb wrestling matches. Nothing worked. He couldn't cheer Grandpa up.

"He's no fun," Taro grumbled.

One summer's day, Mum said, "Let's go on a special adventure."

They got in the car and Mum drove them to Richmond Park.

Taro steered Kiko's pushchair along the side of the hedge, and pointed out interesting things.

"Careful," said Grandpa. "You shouldn't charge along so fast!"

Taro glared and pulled a face at Grandpa's back.
Mum nudged him. "Don't be cheeky!" she whispered.
"What?" Taro asked, keeping an innocent expression
on his face.

"Let's take a break and eat our picnic here," said Mum, kneeling by a large tree stump.

"Pretty!" said Kiko, pointing a podgy finger.

There was a strange creature climbing up to the edge of the stump.

"What's that?" Taro asked.

"A stag beetle!" said Grandpa. His face lit up with pleasure.

"When I was eight, I caught four stag beetles to keep as pets," said Grandpa.

Mum poured him some more water. Grandpa took a sip and swallowed.

"Are they good pets?" Taro asked.

"No, atrocious!" Grandpa admitted. "The big male beetles were full of aggression and knocked the poor smaller ones over!"

"My father roared at me and told me to take them straight back to their home!" Grandpa chuckled. "It was nightfall and I wanted my dinner and a bath, but I obeyed him."

"Your father sounds very strict," said Taro, unwrapping his lunch.

"He wasn't!" laughed Grandpa. "He taught me that we shouldn't interfere with the lives of nature's creatures."

"It's a pleasure to see you smile," said Mum, helping Kiko climb a low branch. "Let's walk somewhere and have a change of scene!"

Taro and Grandpa agreed.

As they walked, Taro noticed a change in Grandpa. His back was straighter, his face looked less tired and grey, and his brow wasn't knotted with tension.

"Doggy!" shouted Kiko.

"That's a baby deer, a fawn."
Grandpa explained. He pulled out
a sketchbook and drew a picture.

"Can I see?" asked Taro.
Grandpa handed it to him.

"I've drawn birds, bears, badgers and, of course, stag beetles!"

"Wow!" said Taro. "Can you teach me to draw?"

Grandpa nodded. "We can come here to practise!"

"Yay!" Taro cheered. "But, how will we get here?"

"The solution is crystal clear," said Grandpa playfully. "We'll both ride bikes!"

"I don't know how," said Taro.

"My mission is to teach you that in addition to art!" said Grandpa.

Taro grinned, and hugged him. "It's official, you're the world's best grandpa!"

Taro and the stag beetle

Review: After reading

Use your assessment from hearing the children read to choose any GPCs, words or tricky words that need additional practice.

Read 1: Decoding

- Discuss the meaning of the following in the context of the characters' expressions:
  page 4 **severe** (*Grandpa looked very serious*)   page 9 **innocent** (*Taro looked as if he hadn't done anything cheeky*)
- Ask the children to read the words and identify the letters that make the sounds:
  /or/ r**oar**ed m**our**ning   /ai/ str**aigh**ter ob**ey**ed br**ea**k
- Starting on page 2, ask the children to take turns to read a sentence. Challenge them to sound out the words silently in their heads.

Read 2: Prosody

- Turn to pages 10 and 11, and focus on reading the spoken words with expression. Explore each character in turn:
  o On page 10, discuss whether Mum would sound enthusiastic or calm, or both, and what Kiko's voice might be like to show her age.
  o On page 11, ask the children to discuss a voice for Taro, and a tone for Grandpa. Ask: How is Grandpa feeling now?
- Ask the children to read the spoken words in groups of four, with each taking a part, then swapping parts too.

Read 3: Comprehension

- Encourage the children to talk about any outings they've enjoyed with their grandparents.
- Ask: What important thing happens at the beginning of the story? (*Grandma dies*) How does Grandpa feel about it? Do his feelings change during the story? How? (e.g. *he is still sad about Grandma, but eventually he's able to be more cheerful.*)
- Encourage the children to explore the characters' feelings by rereading and discussing the following changes.
  o On page 4, ask: Why didn't Grandpa care?
  o On page 6, discuss why Taro **grumbled**. Ask: How is Taro feeling and why?
  o On page 11, ask: Why has Grandpa's face lit up? How is he feeling now? Why?
  o On page 21, discuss how Taro is feeling about Grandpa now, and why.
- Turn to pages 22 and 23. Encourage the children to use the pictures to help them retell the story in their own words.